Life Science

Materials

Cards needing materials other than paper and pencils are:

3, 10, 11—magazines or newspapers to cut from

4—tiny plastic balls or pellets, small seeds

Life Science Card # ______

Your Name: ______

Group Members: ______

Life Science Card # ______

Your Name: ______

Group Members: ______

©2005 by Evan-Moor Corp. • EMC 5006 • Science Cooperative Learning Cards

Science
Cooperative Learning
CARDS

- fold -

- fold -

Life Science

1 Human Thumbs

- Use your pencil to write your name on a sheet of paper. Now have a partner use a long piece of masking tape to tape your thumb to the palm of your hand. Try to write your name again. Could you?

- Think of all the tasks you do with your hands every day. Write down all the ideas your group comes up with. Then circle the tasks that would be impossible to do without your thumbs.

- All primates, including humans, have "opposable" thumbs. That means their thumbs can fold in toward their fingers to grasp objects. Write how you think opposable thumbs helped humans in their evolution.

Life Science   Process Skill: **Experimenting**

---

2 Smell and Taste

- A friend has just told you that your sense of smell and your sense of taste are connected. She says that if you can't smell, then you can't taste. What personal experiences tell you that this is true or not true? Discuss your ideas with your group.

- As a group, design an experiment to determine whether or not smell and taste are connected. Write a list of the materials you will use in your experiment and describe the steps you will follow.

- If there is time and if you have your teacher's permission, collect the materials and conduct your experiment on other members of your group.

Life Science   Process Skill: **Designing an Experiment**

---

3 Living or Nonliving?

- Cut pictures from magazines and newspapers of various objects.

- Which of the objects are living things? Which are nonliving? Which were once living? As a group, sort the pictures into four piles: *Living Things, Nonliving Things, Once Living Things,* and *Not Sure.*

- Discuss with your group how you decided whether or not each object was a living thing. How is a living thing different from a nonliving thing or a once living thing? Write a definition of each.

- Use class resources to find out where each of the objects in the *Not Sure* pile belongs.

Life Science   Process Skill: **Classifying**

---

4 Seed or Non-Seed?

- Imagine that your teacher just gave you a handful of different tiny round objects. Some are seeds and some are just tiny balls of plastic.

- As a group, design an experiment to find out which of these tiny objects are seeds and which are not. Write a list of the materials you will use in your experiment and describe the steps you will follow.

- If there is time and if you have your teacher's permission, conduct your experiment using the tiny objects supplied by your teacher.

Life Science   Process Skill: **Designing an Experiment**

Life Science

Life Science

Life Science

Life Science

6 Basic Needs of Plants

- Like all living things, plants have basic needs that must be met in order to survive. Use class resources to find out the basic needs of plants. Write a list of all the needs you identify.

- Now imagine that another class in your school is trying to grow bean plants in their classroom. But the plants are dying and the students don't know why.

- As a group, write a list of questions you might ask the students in that class about how they have been taking care of the plants. The questions should allow you to figure out why the plants might be dying.

Life Science   Process Skill: **Generating Questions**

8 Getting Oxygen

- All animals need oxygen to live. When oxygen is combined with food the animal eats, energy is created. The animal uses this energy to live.

- Different animals have different ways of getting oxygen. Humans have lungs that take in oxygen from the air. But not all animals have lungs.

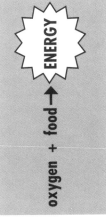

oxygen + food → **ENERGY**

- As a group, use class resources to find out how each of the following animals gets oxygen: squirrel, bird, frog, fish, earthworm, grasshopper. Write about your findings.

Life Science   Process Skill: **Generating Ideas**

5 Plant or Animal?

- Look at pictures of plants and animals in books or magazines.

- Think about what makes a plant different from an animal. Write down some of your ideas. Discuss your ideas with the other members of your group.

- Use your discussion notes to create a Venn diagram showing what characteristics plants and animals have in common, and those which they do not.

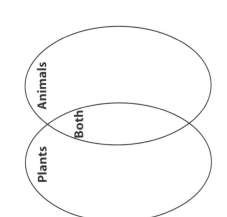

Plants   Both   Animals

Life Science   Process Skill: **Comparing**

7 Basic Needs of Animals

- Like all living things, animals have basic needs that must be met in order to survive. Use class resources to find out the basic needs of animals. Write a list of all the needs you identify.

- Now imagine that another class in your school is trying to raise fish in an aquarium in their classroom. But the fish are dying and the students don't know why.

- Think about what you know about the basic needs of animals. As a group, write a list of ideas you have for why the fish might be dying.

Life Science   Process Skill: **Comparing**

Life Science

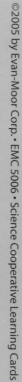

Life Science

Life Science

Life Science

9 Class Pet

- Imagine that your class is considering getting a pet for the classroom. Which pet would you want to keep in the classroom? Why?

- Use class resources to research the needs of the animal you would like to see kept as a class pet. Consider if the animal would do well in your classroom alone over the weekend.

- Write a list of reasons based on your research why you think the animal you chose is the best choice.

- Hold a debate with the other members of your group about which animal would be the best choice.

Life Science   Process Skill: **Communicating**

10 Using Plants and Animals

- Humans have been making use of plants and animals for thousands of years. Both provide humans with food, but that's not all.

- Cut pictures from magazines and newspapers that show objects made of plants and animals.

- As a group, sort the pictures into two categories: *From Plants* and *From Animals*. Discuss the reasons for your decisions.

- Glue the pictures in each group onto a piece of posterboard. Label the pictures to tell what they are and the plant or animal that was used to make them.

Life Science   Process Skill: **Comparing**

11 Fruit or Vegetable?

- Cut pictures from magazines and newspapers of various fruits and vegetables.

- With your group, discuss how fruits and vegetables are different from each other.

- Use class resources to research and then write a definition of each.

- As a group, sort the pictures into three piles: *Fruits, Vegetables,* and *Not Sure.*

- Use class resources to find out where each object in the *Not Sure* pile belongs.

Life Science   Process Skill: **Classifying**

12 Plant Parts

leaves

roots

- The vegetables that people eat are parts of plants. Some are roots, some are stems, and some are leaves.

- With your group, brainstorm a list of vegetables. Write the name of each vegetable on a separate piece of paper.

- Sort the pieces of paper into four piles: *Roots, Stems, Leaves,* and *Not Sure.*

- Use class resources to find out where each of the vegetables in the *Not Sure* pile belongs.

Life Science   Process Skill: **Classifying**

Life Science

Life Science

Life Science

Life Science

13 — Making Food & Using Food

- Plants use the energy in sunlight to make food.

  Carbon Dioxide + Water + Sunlight → Food + Oxygen

- Animals use food to get the energy they need to live.

  Oxygen + Food → Energy + Carbon Dioxide + Water

- Divide your group in half. Have each group use simple materials to make a model of one of the processes described above. Make sure that the same materials are used to represent the same substances in each model.

Life Science   Process Skill: **Making Models**

---

14 — Growth and Change

- One characteristic of all living things is that they grow and change over time.

- Have each member of your group choose a different living thing. It can be a kind of plant, animal, or fungus, or even a microorganism.

- Use class resources to find out how your organism changes over its lifetime.

- Draw a series of cartoon panels that show how your organism changes over time. Compare your cartoon panel with the other panels in your group.

Life Science   Process Skill: **Sequencing**

---

15 — Seasonal Changes

- With your group, discuss how the weather changes from season to season where you live.

- Many plants and animals go through seasonal changes. Some trees lose their leaves in the winter. Many animals shed their heavy winter coats in the summer.

- Choose one plant or animal to research. Use class resources to find out what seasonal changes that plant or animal goes through. The changes might be in appearance or in behavior. How do the changes help it survive? Write about your findings.

- Share your information with the other members of your group.

Life Science   Process Skill: **Inferring**

---

16 — Eggs or Babies?

- Some animals, like chickens, lay eggs. The young animals develop in the shells and come out later. Other animals, like cats, have live young.

- With your group, brainstorm a list of animals. Write the name of each animal on a separate piece of paper.

- As a group, sort the pieces of paper into three piles: *Eggs, Live Young,* and *Not Sure.* Discuss what you are basing your decisions on.

- Use class resources to find out where each of the animals in the *Not Sure* pile belongs.

- Discuss the differences between the animals that lay eggs and those that have live babies.

Life Science   Process Skill: **Classifying**

Life Science

Life Science

Life Science

Life Science

18 Adaptations

- An adaptation is a physical structure or behavior that helps an organism survive in its environment. Fins help a fish to swim through water. Hiding underground during the daytime when it's hot helps a kangaroo rat stay cool.

- Think of a plant or animal with a special adaptation. Draw a picture of the organism and label or describe the adaptation. Write an explanation of how the adaptation helps the organism survive in its environment.

- Share your picture and explanation with the other members of your group. Discuss what the different adaptations have in common.

Life Science   Process Skill: **Communicating**

20 Camouflage

- Some animals have special shapes, colors, or patterns that help them blend in with their surroundings. This characteristic is known as *camouflage.* By blending in with their surroundings, the animals can avoid being eaten by hungry predators, or they can stalk prey.

- On a piece of paper, draw and color an insect that would be camouflaged in one of these places: on a plant stem, on a tree trunk, or in a pile of dead leaves.

- Cut out your insect and try to camouflage it outdoors on the surface it was meant to imitate. Have another member of your group try to find it. Then try to find the insects hidden by others.

Life Science   Process Skill: **Making Models**

17 Plant Behavior

- You probably know that animals have certain behaviors. But did you know that plants do, too? The following picture shows what happens to a plant that has been tipped over and left in that position.

- With your group, discuss the changes you notice in the way the tipped-over plant is growing. How might these changes help the plant meet its basic needs and survive?

- Imagine the pot is tipped over to the right. Draw a picture showing what the plant would do.

Life Science   Process Skill: **Inferring**

19 Adaptation and Environment

- Think about a fish, a cactus, and a polar bear. Now think about the environment where each organism lives.

- How is each organism specially adapted to live in its environment? What physical characteristics help it survive in its environment? What behaviors help it survive? Use class resources to help you find the answers to these questions. Write an explanation for each.

- Discuss the following with your group: Could a polar bear live in the desert? Could a cactus grow in the ocean? Could a fish live in the desert sand? Why or why not?

Life Science   Process Skill: **Applying Knowledge**

Life Science

Life Science

Life Science

Life Science

21 Animal Senses

- Animals use their senses to find out what is going on in their environment. These senses include sight, smell, taste, hearing, and touch.

- As a group, make a concept map on a large sheet of paper to show how a rabbit might use its five senses to collect information about its environment.

Process Skill: **Concept Mapping**

Life Science

22 Animals at Night

- As a group, make a list of animals that are active only at night. Don't forget insects!

- Use class resources to help find out why each animal is active at night instead of during the day. How does being active at night help the animal survive? As a group, discuss your findings.

- Have each group member choose one animal from the list. Draw and label a picture showing what body part or parts help the animal sense its environment in the dark.

- Share your picture and information with the other group members.

Process Skill: **Communicating**

Life Science

23 Locomotion

- All animals move in some way. Most animals move around to find food, water, shelter, and even air.

- Think about how each of the following kinds of animals moves from one place to another: fish, birds, mammals, insects.

- Have each group member choose one kind of animal. Draw and label a picture showing how the animal you chose moves around.

- As a group, compare all the drawings. Discuss what body parts are used for movement. Tell how the movement is suited to the animal's environment.

Process Skill: **Comparing**

Life Science

24 Body Coverings

- Different animals have different kinds of body coverings, including fur, feathers, and scales.

- As a group, brainstorm a list of different kinds of animals. Include birds, fish, amphibians, reptiles, insects, and mammals.

- Discuss the kind of body covering each animal has. Do animals from the same group have the same kind of body covering?

- Write an explanation for the following questions: What is the purpose of a body covering? How does each kind of body covering help the animal survive in its environment?

Process Skill: **Inferring**

Life Science

Life Science

Life Science

Life Science

Life Science

25 Animal Classification

- The sorting of organisms into different groups based on their characteristics is known as *classification*.

- Use class resources to find out the main characteristics of animals in the following classification groups: insects, fish, amphibians, reptiles, birds, and mammals.

- Now, imagine that your group has received a letter from a student in another state. The student has found an animal but doesn't know how to classify it.

- As a group, write a list of questions you could ask the student in order to find out which classification group the animal belongs to.

Life Science   Process Skill: **Generating Questions**

26 Frogs and Toads

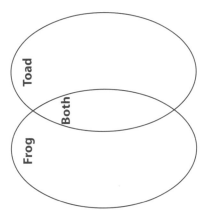

Frog   Both   Toad

- What is the difference between a frog and a toad? Brainstorm a list of ideas with your group. Think about where the animals live as well as what they look like.

- Use class resources to find out all the things that make a frog different from a toad.

- Make a Venn diagram to show what the two animals have in common and how they differ.

Life Science   Process Skill: **Comparing**

27 Animals That Fly

- Many animals can walk, run, or even hop. But only certain animals can fly.

- With your group, brainstorm a list of animals that can fly. Write the names on separate pieces of paper.

- Sort the pieces of paper into different piles. Each pile should form a different classification group.

- As a group, discuss the following questions: What groups of animals have members that can fly? What groups do not have members that can fly?

- What body part do all animals use to fly? Write about how that body part differs from one group to another.

Life Science   Process Skill: **Classifying**

28 Ecosystems

- All the living and nonliving things that interact in an environment make up an ecosystem.

- Go outside to the area selected by your teacher. Write down everything you see in the ecosystem.

- Back in the classroom, write each thing your group observed on a separate piece of paper. As a group, sort all the living things into one pile. Put all the nonliving things in another pile.

- How do the living things in the ecosystem interact with one another? How do they interact with the nonliving parts of the ecosystem? Discuss your ideas with your group.

Life Science   Process Skill: **Observing**

Life Science

Life Science

Life Science

Life Science

29 Herbivores and Carnivores

- As a group, brainstorm a list of all the different plants and animals you might find in a grassland habitat. Draw a picture that shows the grassland scene.

- A producer is an organism that uses sunlight to make its own food. A consumer is an organism that eats plants or animals. There are two kinds of consumers: herbivores and carnivores. A herbivore is an animal that gets the energy it needs by eating plants. A carnivore is an animal that gets the energy it needs by eating other animals.

- Label your picture to show the producers, herbivores, and carnivores.

Life Science   Process Skill: **Classifying**

30 Food Chains

- As a group, brainstorm a list of all the different plants and animals you might find in a forest habitat. Think of animals from each classification group. Draw simple pictures of each plant and animal on a separate piece of paper. Label the pictures.

- A food chain is a diagram that shows the feeding relationships between plants and animals living together in the same habitat.

Grass → Rabbit → Fox

- Using your pictures, create food chains that show some of the feeding relationships in the forest.

Life Science   Process Skill: **Making Models**

31 Changes in an Ecosystem

- Think about a forest ecosystem. As a group, brainstorm a list of all the different plants and animals you might find there. Think about the nonliving parts of the forest as well. Draw a picture that shows all the living and nonliving parts of the forest ecosystem.

- Imagine now that an insect pest came into the forest and wiped out most of the grasses that grow on the forest floor. As a group, discuss how this change might affect other parts of the forest ecosystem.

- Write a prediction of what might happen in the forest as a result of the grasses being wiped out.

Life Science   Process Skill: **Predicting**

32 The End of the Dinosaurs

- The dinosaurs died out millions of years ago. Based on evidence found today, this is what scientists think happened: 65 million years ago, a meteor from space struck Earth. This impact sent lots of dust up into the atmosphere. The dust blocked out most of the sunlight that once reached Earth's plants. Without much light, most of the plants died out. With nothing to eat, the dinosaurs eventually died out, too.

- Draw a series of cartoon panels that show the story of what scientists think happened to the dinosaurs as a result of the change to their environment. Label each panel to show what is happening.

Life Science   Process Skill: **Sequencing**

Life Science

Life Science

Life Science

Life Science

Earth Science

Materials

Cards needing materials other than paper and pencils are:

6—magnifier, salt

7—magnifier, soil sample

9, 14, 17—magazines and newspapers to cut from

19—thermometer, rain gauge, barometer, wind vane or anemometer

28—cardboard or plastic product packaging

Earth Science   Card # _____

Science
Cooperative Learning
CARDS

Your Name: _____

Group Members: _____

Earth Science   Card # _____

Science
Cooperative Learning
CARDS

Your Name: _____

Group Members: _____

- fold -

- fold -

Earth Science

2 | Earth's Surface

- The top layer of the Earth is called the *crust*. It is the thinnest layer. What is the crust made of?

- As a group, brainstorm a list of things that make up the Earth's crust. Base your ideas on your experiences of being outdoors.

- Write the name of each thing you listed on a separate piece of paper. As a group, sort the pieces of paper into two piles: *Living* and *Nonliving*. Discuss how the living things depend on the nonliving things.

- Earth's crust is always changing. What evidence do you have that this is true? Discuss your ideas as a group.

Earth Science Process Skill: **Communicating**

---

4 | Earth's Rocks

- The Earth contains many different kinds of rocks. Scientists classify rocks into three main groups. How a rock is classified depends on how it was formed.

- Use class resources to find out the names of the three main groups of rocks. Write about the characteristics of each group and how each is formed. Describe the relationship between each group.

- With your group, use what you find out to make a concept map on a large piece of paper showing the three different groups of rocks and how they are related.

Earth Science Process Skill: **Concept Mapping**

---

1 | Earth's Structure

- Earth is shaped like a ball, or sphere. What would you find if you could dig down to the center of the Earth?

- Use class resources to find out about the different layers that make up the Earth. How many layers are there? How is one layer different from another?

- Use what you learn to draw a series of cartoon panels showing how conditions would change as you moved towards the center of the Earth. Each panel should show the journey through one Earth layer. Work together with your group to plan and design each panel.

Earth Science Process Skill: **Sequencing**

---

3 | Landforms

- The surface of the Earth's crust is always changing.

- Forces such as crustal deformations, volcano eruptions, deposits of sediment, and erosion bring about most surface changes that create different landforms.

- Choose one of the following landforms and research to find out which force made it:
  - Grand Canyon — Mississippi Delta
  - Hawaiian Islands — Rocky Mountains

- Draw a series of pictures that show how your landform was created. Label the pictures to tell what happened.

- Share your pictures with the other group members.

Earth Science Process Skill: **Sequencing**

Earth Science

Earth Science

Earth Science

Earth Science

6 Salt Crystals

- All rocks are mixtures of minerals. Salt is an example of one of the minerals found in Earth's crust. Like all minerals, salt is made up of crystals. Crystals come in different shapes, but all have flat sides.

- Use a magnifier to observe a few grains of salt. Draw a picture showing the shape of the crystals you see. How many sides does a salt crystal have?

- Use class resources to find out some of the other crystal shapes. Work with the other members of your group to construct models of different crystal shapes using sheets of cardboard and tape.

Earth Science   Process Skill: **Observing**

8 Importance of Soil

- Most of us take soil for granted. It's just dirt, right? But without soil, there could be no life on Earth.

- Imagine a rainforest habitat. As a group, draw a large picture of all the things found there, both living and nonliving.

- Now imagine that all the soil is removed from the rainforest floor. What other parts of the rainforest habitat would be affected by this change? What could live in the rainforest without soil? Discuss your ideas with your group. Label the drawing to tell how each part of the rainforest would be affected by the change.

Earth Science   Process Skill: **Inferring**

5 Sedimentary Rock

- Sedimentary rock is one of the three main groups of rocks. Sedimentary rock is formed when sediments—bits of rock and shell and other materials—fall to the bottom of lakes and oceans. Over many years, the layers are pressed together to form sedimentary rock.

- Discuss with your group what classroom materials you could use to construct a model of a sedimentary rock. Once your group has decided on a model, ask your teacher for permission to construct the model.

- Share your model with another group. Discuss what your model has in common with their model.

Earth Science   Process Skill: **Making Models**

7 Soil

- Much of Earth's surface is covered with soil. You have probably seen soil and worked in soil before. But do you know what soil is made of?

- With your group, brainstorm a list of things you think make up soil. If possible, examine a soil sample using a magnifier and list the things you see.

- Then use class resources to find out what things make up soil. With your group, make a concept map on a large piece of paper showing the relationship between rocks, soil, water, and plants.

Earth Science   Process Skill: **Concept Mapping**

Earth Science

Earth Science

Earth Science

Earth Science

10 Lakes and Oceans

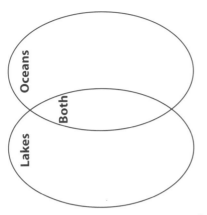

Lakes   Both   Oceans

- Lakes and oceans are both bodies of water found on Earth's surface. But they are very different.
- As a group, brainstorm a list about the characteristics of a lake. Then brainstorm a list of qualities that describe an ocean. Use class resources to check your ideas.
- Create a Venn diagram to show what characteristics lakes and oceans have in common, and how they differ.

Earth Science   Process Skill: **Comparing**

---

12 Water on the Move

- Water moves through nature as part of the water cycle. There are three basic steps to the water cycle:
  1) Liquid water on Earth's surface evaporates and rises into the air as water vapor.
  2) High up in the air, the water vapor condenses to form tiny droplets of water, which we see as clouds.
  3) Eventually, the drops get bigger and fall back to Earth as precipitation.
- As a group, make a concept map on a large piece of paper showing how the three steps of the water cycle work together to move water through nature.

Earth Science   Process Skill: **Concept Mapping**

---

9 Water on Earth

- As a group, brainstorm a list of all the different places on Earth where water can be found.
  - Cut pictures from magazines and newspapers or draw pictures that show water in nature.
  - As a group, sort the pictures into different piles based on common characteristics. Discuss what all the pictures in each pile have in common.
  - Glue the pictures in each pile to one section of a posterboard. Label each group of pictures to show what the pictures have in common.

Earth Science   Process Skill: **Organizing**

---

11 Changing Water

- Water in nature changes form in the following ways:
  - Evaporation—liquid water changes into a gas called *water vapor*. This gas floats through the air.
  - Condensation—water vapor in the air changes back into drops of liquid water.
  - Freezing—liquid water changes into solid ice.
  - Melting—solid ice changes into liquid water when warmed.
- With your group, brainstorm a list of examples of when you have seen each of these changes.
- Make a poster showing your personal experiences with each of these processes.

Earth Science   Process Skill: **Communicating**

Earth Science

Earth Science

Earth Science

Earth Science

14 Seasons

- Cut out pictures from magazines and newspapers that show nature during different seasons.

- As a group, sort the pictures into four piles: *Spring, Summer, Fall,* and *Winter.*

- With your group, discuss the different seasons you experience during the year where you live. How cold does it get in winter? Does it snow? How warm does it get in summer?

- Write about the changes the plants and animals in your area go through as the seasons change.

Earth Science   Process Skill: **Organizing**

16 Staying Warm or Cool

- Humans are most comfortable when the temperature is not too hot and not too cold. And yet people live in extremely cold and extremely hot places.

- As a group, brainstorm a list of ways that people in cold climates stay warm. Then brainstorm a list of ways that people in hot climates stay cool.

- Animals can't change their environments as easily as humans can. But they do have their own ways of surviving in hot and cold places. Use class resources to find out how animals stay warm in the Arctic and cool in the desert.

Earth Science   Process Skill: **Communicating**

13 Dating Fossils

- Fossils are the remains of plants or animals that lived long ago. After the organisms died, their bodies were buried in layer after layer of mud.

- Fossils do not come with dates printed on them. But scientists have other ways of figuring out how old one fossil is compared to another.

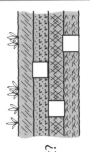

- Look at the fossils in the dig site to the right. How could you tell which fossil was the oldest and which was the most recent? Discuss your ideas with your group.

- Write about how fossils give us a picture of life in the past.

Earth Science   Process Skill: **Inferring**

15 Hot and Cold

- What are the hottest times of day where you live? What are the hottest times of the year where you live? Come to an agreement with your group.

- As a group, brainstorm a list of ideas for why the temperatures are the hottest during this time of day and during this time of year.

- Once your list of ideas is complete, use class resources to check your ideas. Were they correct?

- Repeat this exercise for the coldest times of the day and year.

- Write about why there are different seasons.

Earth Science   Process Skill: **Generating Ideas**

Earth Science

Earth Science

Earth Science

Earth Science

18 Wind

- Wind is moving air. Weather forecasters like to measure how hard the wind is blowing. They can use this information to make predictions about the weather.

- Imagine that a weather forecaster called you on the phone and asked you to describe the strength of the wind around your home or school. What clues from the environment could you use to help you figure out how hard the wind was blowing? Discuss your ideas with your group.

- With your group, make a poster showing how you might know when the wind is blowing hard, when it is blowing a little, and when it is not blowing at all.

Earth Science   Process Skill: **Problem Solving**

20 Weather Map

- A weather map is a map that uses symbols to show some of the weather conditions in an area.

- Find a weather map in your local newspaper. It can be a map of your local area, or a map of the whole United States. Examine the map with your group. Use the legend to figure out what the different map symbols mean.

- Use class resources to learn more about weather fronts and areas of high and low pressure.

- Use the map and what you learned to write about the weather shown on the map.

Earth Science   Process Skill: **Interpreting Diagrams**

17 Clouds

- Cut pictures from magazines that show different kinds of clouds.

- As a group, sort the pictures into piles of similar-looking clouds.

- Use class resources to identify each pile of pictures as one of the four main kinds of clouds: stratus, cumulus, cumulonimbus, or cirrus.

- Make a poster showing the different kinds of clouds. Label each kind. Write a description of what shape they are and where in the sky each kind is located.

Earth Science   Process Skill: **Comparing**

19 Weather Data

- What conditions do you think about when someone asks you, "How's the weather?"

- Some basic weather conditions include temperature, rainfall, air pressure, wind, and cloud cover.

- Use simple weather instruments to collect data at your school for one week. Record your data on a chart.
  - Thermometer: temperature
  - Rain gauge: rainfall
  - Barometer: air pressure
  - Wind vane or anemometer: wind direction or speed

- Use the data to write a comparison of the weather at the beginning of the week and at the end.

Earth Science   Process Skill: **Collecting Data**

Earth Science

Earth Science

Earth Science

Earth Science

22 Moon Phases

- The moon appears to change shape as it moves through its 28-day orbit around Earth. This is because sunlight shines on different amounts of the moon as it travels around Earth.

- Draw a large copy of the diagram shown below. Use class resources to help you finish drawing the different moon phases in the correct order as it orbits Earth.

- As a group, discuss how the phases of the moon change during the month.

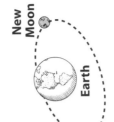

New Moon

Earth

Sun

Earth Science   Process Skill: **Sequencing**

---

24 Solar System

- Our solar system is made up of a star—our sun—and nine planets that revolve around it. Earth is one of those planets.

- As a group, use class resources to find out the names and positions of the other eight planets in our solar system. Find a scale that shows the "relative" size of each planet. That means the size of a planet when compared to the size of the other planets.

- Use what you find out to create a model of the solar system. Put the planets in the correct order and make each planet the correct size relative to the other planets.

Earth Science   Process Skill: **Making Models**

---

21 Changing Shadows

- Go outside to the playground area with your group. What shadows can you see? Draw one object and the shadow it casts. Also draw where the sun is located in relation to the object and the shadow.

- An hour later, go back to the same spot. How has the shadow changed? Draw the object, shadow, and sun again. Compare your two drawings.

- Now compare your drawings with the drawings of other members in your group. Do you see a pattern? Write a prediction about the shape and position of the shadow an hour from now. Tell where the sun will be then in relation to the object.

Earth Science   Process Skill: **Predicting**

---

23 Spacesuit

- The moon might look like just a very dry, rocky version of Earth. But conditions on the moon are very different from conditions here on Earth.

- Use class resources to help you make a list of the ways the moon is different from Earth.

- Look at the picture of the astronaut in the spacesuit.

- What can you infer about the spacesuit? What must it provide the astronaut with? Discuss ideas with your group.

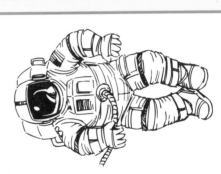

Earth Science   Process Skill: **Inferring**

Earth Science

Science
Cooperative Learning
CARDS

Earth Science

Science
Cooperative Learning
CARDS

Earth Science

Science
Cooperative Learning
CARDS

Earth Science

Science
Cooperative Learning
CARDS

25   Earth and Mars

- Earth and Mars are two planets in our solar system.

- Use class resources to research some basic facts about each planet. Take notes about each planet's diameter, length of a day and year, distance from the sun, and number of moons.

- With your group, use the information you collect to create a Venn diagram comparing Earth and Mars.

- Write about how the planets are different from each other and about how they are similar.

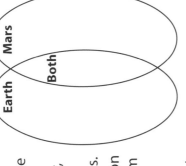

Earth Science   Process Skill: **Comparing**

26   Exploring Space

- Every year, the U.S. government spends billions of dollars exploring space.

- Using class resources, have half of your group research the benefits of space exploration. The other half will research the costs and risks of space exploration.

- Hold a debate with your group members. Half of the group should take the position that space exploration is worth the cost and risk, no matter what has been found so far. The other members should take the position that there are not enough benefits from space exploration to overcome the costs and risks.

Earth Science   Process Skill: **Communicating**

27   Playground Litter

- Litter is any trash that has not been thrown away properly. Litter is ugly and pollutes the environment.

- Go outside to the playground area of your school. Look around for litter. Write down the name of every piece of litter you see. If you have your teacher's permission, collect the litter and throw it away.

- Back in the classroom, write the name of each piece of litter on a separate piece of paper. With your group, sort the pieces of paper into different piles according to the source of the litter. Write about what action you might be able to take to reduce the amount of litter on your playground.

Earth Science   Process Skill: **Classifying**

28   Packaging

- Most products sold in stores come in some sort of packaging. Packaging is the cardboard or plastic that protects the product and tells you about it. But packaging is wasteful because once the product is unwrapped, the packaging is just thrown away.

- Look at the packaging on some of the items your teacher has brought in. With your group, brainstorm a list of ideas about how you might be able to use less packaging to protect the products.

- As a group, create new packaging for one of the products that is less wasteful. Share your "new improved" packaging with another group.

Earth Science   Process Skill: **Problem Solving**

Earth Science

Earth Science

Earth Science

Earth Science

30 Using Water

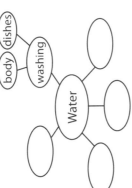

- Water is one of Earth's most important natural resources. Like many of the other resources, it is limited in supply.

- With your group, brainstorm a list of ways that you use water every day. Use your list to make a concept map on a large piece of paper showing your water usage.

- Now, extend the concept map to include ways you might be able to reduce the total amount of water you use. Think of ways you could reuse some of the water.

Process Skill: **Concept Mapping**

32 Alternative Energy

- Fossil fuels are the most commonly used sources of energy. But they are in limited supply. So scientists are always looking for other "alternative" sources of energy.

- Have each member of your group use class resources to research one of the following kinds of alternative energy: solar, wind, hydroelectric, or biofuel. Write a list of reasons why the kind of energy you researched is the best choice.

- Hold a debate in which each member of your group makes an argument for why the source of energy he or she researched is the best choice.

Process Skill: **Communicating**

29 Reduce, Reuse, Recycle

- Earth's natural resources—including wood, paper, metal, and plastic—are in limited supply. We can conserve natural resources by following the three *R*'s:
  – reduce the amount of resources we use
  – reuse old objects in a new way
  – recycle materials that can be reworked into new materials

- With your group, brainstorm a list of ideas for how you can put the three *R*'s to work in your classroom. What objects can be recycled or reused in a new way instead of thrown out? How might you reduce the amount of paper you use every day?

Process Skill: **Generating Ideas**

31 Fossil Fuels

- Fossil fuels are fuels that were formed from the remains of dead plants and animals that lived long ago. Fossil fuels include oil, coal, and natural gas. Gasoline is made from oil.

- With your group, brainstorm a list of ways you and your family use fossil fuels. Use class resources as needed to help you find out what kind of things each fossil fuel is used for.

- Write each thing and fossil fuel type on a separate piece of paper. As a group, sort the pieces of paper into piles by fuel type. Discuss which kind of fossil fuel your group uses the most.

Process Skill: **Organizing**

Earth Science

Earth Science

Earth Science

Earth Science

Physical Science

Materials

Cards needing materials other than paper and pencils are:

3—balance or scale

5—sugar, salt, sand, powder, pepper, baking soda

6—salt, sand

7—ball of clay

16—ball of clay or foil

17—eggs, packaging supplies

21—ice cubes

28, 29—bar magnets

Physical Science   Card # _____

Your Name: _____

Group Members: _____

Physical Science   Card # _____

Your Name: _____

Group Members: _____

Science Cooperative Learning CARDS

- fold -

- - - fold - - -

Physical Science

2 Volume

- Volume is the amount of space that an object takes up.

- The volume of a block-shaped object can be determined by measuring its length, width, and height and then multiplying the three numbers together.

- Find a book or other block-shaped object in the classroom. Use a ruler to measure its length, width, and height. Use these numbers to calculate its volume.

Physical Science   Process Skill: **Measuring**

---

4 Air Is Matter

- You use your five senses to detect most of the matter, or "stuff," around you. You see a bird, you smell a baking pie, you taste a strawberry, you hear a passing truck. But what about matter that you can't directly see, hear, feel, smell, or taste?

- Air is invisible. But still somehow you know that it is all around you. How do you know?

- With your group, brainstorm a list of ways that you know air is all around you. Beside each item on the list, write the evidence you have that it exists. Then list the senses you use to detect the presence of air in each case.

Physical Science   Process Skill: **Generating Ideas**

---

1 Mass

- Mass is a measure of the amount of matter, or "stuff," in an object. You are made up of more "stuff" than a golf ball. So, you have more mass than a golf ball.

- Mass can be measured using a balance or scale.

- Look around the classroom. With your group, brainstorm a list of objects you see. Write the name of each object on a separate piece of paper. Put the pieces in a pile.

- Draw two pieces of paper out of the pile. Predict which has more mass. Use a scale or balance to find out.

Physical Science   Process Skill: **Measuring**

---

3 Density

- Density is a measure of how close together the matter, or "stuff," in an object is packed. Density can be found by dividing an object's mass by its volume.

- Find a book or other block-shaped object in the classroom. Use a balance or scale to find its mass. Use a ruler to measure its length, width, and height. Use these numbers to calculate its volume.

- Divide the object's mass by its volume to find its density. Make a chart and compare the densities of different objects in the classroom. Write a comparison about the most dense and the least dense object.

Physical Science   Process Skill: **Comparing**

Physical Science

Physical Science

Physical Science

Physical Science

6 Separating a Mixture

- Imagine that your group has been handed a container with a mixture of sand and salt. You know that salt dissolves in water but sand does not. How might you use this information to separate the two substances?

- Brainstorm some ideas with your group.

- As a group, decide on a plan. Write a description of the steps you will use to test your plan. Then ask your teacher for permission to try it out. Did it work? If not, write a list of other ideas for separating the salt and sand.

Physical Science   Process Skill: **Problem Solving**

8 Periodic Table

- The periodic table is a chart that shows all the different kinds of pure substances—called "elements"—on Earth. The elements are grouped according to their properties or characteristics.

- Use resource books to find a copy of the periodic table. Have each member of your group choose one element to report on. Each report should include the following information:
  - the element's name;
  - the element's symbol;
  - the element's atomic number; and
  - the element's atomic mass.

Physical Science   Process Skill: **Communicating**

5 Dissolving Substances

- Some substances dissolve in water. Others do not. The ability to dissolve in water is one property of a substance.

- As a group, test different substances to see if they dissolve in water. Use the substances provided by your teacher. These may include sugar, salt, sand, talcum powder, pepper, and baking soda.

Substance	Dissolve?
salt	

- Stir the same amount of each substance into a cup of water using a stirring stick. Which substances dissolved? Record your data on a chart.

Physical Science   Process Skill: **Collecting Data**

7 Atoms

- An atom is the smallest particle of a substance. Every kind of pure substance has its own kind of atom. A gold atom is different from a silver atom.

- Every atom is made up of the same basic parts—protons, neutrons, and electrons. The atoms of different substances have a different number of these parts.

- As a group, use classroom materials to create a model of a carbon atom.

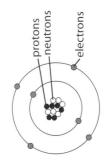

Carbon Atom

Physical Science   Process Skill: **Making Models**

Physical Science

Physical Science

Physical Science

Physical Science

Gravity

10

- Gravity is the force that attracts one object toward another. Gravity exists between the sun and all the planets. It's what keeps the planets in orbit around the sun. Gravity also exists between Earth and all the objects on Earth.

- With your group, brainstorm a list of examples of how gravity is at work all around you. Think about how gravity affects objects that are moving and objects that are not moving. How does it affect you? How does it affect objects thrown into the air?

- Make a poster showing several of your group's examples.

Physical Science   Process Skill: **Communicating**

Sink or Float?

12

- Some objects sink in water. Others float.

- Collect different small objects from around the classroom. You will place these objects in water to see if they sink or float. Make sure you have your teacher's permission to test each object.

Object	Prediction: float or not?	Result: float or not?

- Before you start your experiment, make a prediction about each object: Do you think it will sink or float?

- Perform your experiment and record your data on a chart.

Physical Science   Process Skill: **Experimenting**

Changing Matter

9

- A physical change to matter happens when a substance changes form but doesn't turn into a new substance. A physical change can be reversed. A chemical change to matter happens when a substance turns into another kind of substance. This change cannot be reversed.

- Compare the following two changes to matter:
  – paper burning
  – water freezing into ice
  - As a group, discuss which change is physical and which is chemical. Why do you think so?

- Brainstorm a list of other physical and chemical changes to matter.

Physical Science   Process Skill: **Comparing**

Air Resistance

11

- Air is made up of tiny particles of matter too small to see. You can think of air particles as tiny floating golf balls. As objects fall through the air, they run into these tiny particles of air. Each particle they hit slows down the speed at which they fall. This phenomenon is known as air resistance.

- Hold your pencil up and drop it. How could you use air resistance to make the pencil fall more slowly? With your group, write a list of some ideas.

- Use simple materials to test out some of your ideas. Which one worked the best? Why do you think it worked so well? Share your results with another group.

Physical Science   Process Skill: **Experimenting**

Physical Science

Physical Science

Physical Science

Physical Science

14 Forces

A force is a push or a pull. A force can make an object start moving or stop moving. It can also make an object change speed or direction.

- With your group, discuss ways that forces are at work in some of your favorite sports. You might discuss baseball, soccer, cycling, skating, gymnastics, or others. In each case, consider where force is applied and which objects start or stop moving, change direction, or change speed.

- Record your ideas on a chart.

Sport	Where Force Is Applied	How Object Moves

Physical Science   Process Skill: **Communicating**

---

13 Make It Float

- Some objects sink in water. Others float.

- Place a small ball of clay in a container of water. Record what happens to it.

- With your group, brainstorm ideas for ways you could make the clay float instead of sink. Decide on a few ideas to test.

- With your teacher's permission, complete your tests. Which ideas worked? Share your solution with another group. Did they solve the problem the same way your group did?

Physical Science   Process Skill: **Experimenting**

---

16 Pendulum

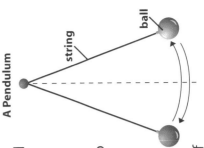

A Pendulum

- A pendulum is a ball attached to the end of a string that swings back and forth when you let it go.

- Make a pendulum by attaching a paper clip to a piece of string. Use foil or clay to form a ball around the clip.

- What determines the time it takes the pendulum to swing back and forth once? Is it the weight of the ball? The height you release it from? The length of the string? Experiment to find out. Write about your findings.

Physical Science   Process Skill: **Experimenting**

---

15 Friction

- Slide a stapler across your desk. Does it slide easily? Now slide the stapler across a carpet. Does it slide more easily? Less easily? Repeat this experiment with other objects. Record your observations.

- Friction is a force that is produced when one object rubs against another object. The rougher the objects rubbing together, the greater the friction.

- As a group, discuss the results of your experiments. Based on your observations, write about how friction affects motion.

Physical Science   Process Skill: **Applying Knowledge**

Physical Science

Physical Science

Physical Science

Physical Science

18 Speed

- Speed is the rate at which an object travels. To find speed, divide the total distance traveled by the time it took to travel the distance.

$$\text{Speed} = \frac{\text{Distance Traveled}}{\text{Time It Took}}$$

- Use this equation to determine the speed at which each of the following cars traveled. Record your results in miles per hour.

Car	Distance Traveled	Time It Took
Orange	120 miles	3 hours
Blue	100 miles	2 hours
Red	140 miles	4 hours
Green	275 miles	5 hours

Physical Science   Process Skill: **Using Numbers**

20 Insulators and Conductors

- A conductor is a material that allows heat energy to move through it easily. An insulator is a material that doesn't allow heat energy to move through it easily.

- With your group, brainstorm a list of insulators and conductors. Think about your experiences with heat or hot objects and how different materials protected you from the heat. Then think about other materials that you wanted to get hot. Also consider materials that protect cold objects from heat.

- Beside each item, describe what the insulator or conductor material is made of. How might the material allow or prevent the movement of heat?

Physical Science   Process Skill: **Inferring**

17 Egg Drop

- Eggs have a very thin shell and are easily broken.

- Imagine that your group has been asked to design some sort of contraption that would protect an egg from breaking as it fell from 10 feet up in the air.

- Brainstorm some ideas with your group. Pick the best idea and get your teacher's permission to collect the materials and build the contraption.

- Test your contraption. Did it work? If not, what do you think was the problem? Work with your group to redesign your contraption and test it again.

Physical Science   Process Skill: **Problem Solving**

19 Heat Sources

- Heat is a form of energy. With your group, brainstorm a list of different sources of heat. Use the information to create a concept map on a large sheet of paper.

- Most heat energy is produced when another form of energy is changed into heat energy. For example, in a toaster, electrical energy is changed into heat energy.

- Extend the concept map to show what form of energy is used to produce heat for each source.

Physical Science   Process Skill: **Concept Mapping**

Physical Science

Physical Science

Physical Science

Physical Science

22 Shipping a Snowball

- Imagine that you have been asked to ship a snowball to a friend of yours in another state. The snowball must be able to make the trip without melting too much.

- With your group, brainstorm a list of ways you might pack the snowball so that it would not melt too much before arriving. Describe the materials you would use. Explain what these materials do and why they are good choices.

- Write a report about your best idea. Include labeled drawings of your idea. Share your report with another group. How do their ideas compare to yours?

Physical Science　　　　Process Skill: **Problem Solving**

24 Potential and Kinetic Energy

- Kinetic energy is the energy of motion. A rolling ball has kinetic energy. Potential energy is stored energy. A rock at the top of a cliff has potential energy.

- A roller coaster shows how potential and kinetic energy can change back and forth. A roller-coaster car at the top of a hill has potential energy. As the car moves down the hill, its potential energy is changed to kinetic energy, and so on as it moves up and down the hills.

- As a group, draw a simple roller coaster. Then draw a car at several different places on the track. Add labels to show where the car's potential and kinetic energy are changing.

Physical Science　　　　Process Skill: **Applying Knowledge**

21 Melting Ice Cube

- If you set an ice cube out on your desk for a few hours, it will melt. That's because heat energy from the air would warm it up, causing it to turn from solid to liquid. How could you slow down the speed at which the ice cube melted?

- With your group, brainstorm some ideas for ways to keep the ice cube solid for as long as possible. You can only use common classroom materials, not a freezer or other appliance.

- If you have your teacher's permission, test out some of your ideas. Write a description of what you did. Explain why it worked so well.

Physical Science　　　　Process Skill: **Experimenting**

23 Delivering Hot Pizza

- Imagine that you are a pizza delivery person. You must get a hot pizza from the oven to a customer on the other side of town without the pizza cooling off too much.

- With your group, brainstorm a list of ways you might pack the pizza so that it won't cool down too much on the trip. Describe the materials you would use. Explain what these materials do and why they are good choices.

- Write a report about your best idea. Include labeled drawings of your idea. Share your report with another group. How do their ideas compare to yours?

Physical Science　　　　Process Skill: **Problem Solving**

Physical Science

Physical Science

Physical Science

Physical Science

26 Making Electricity

- Do you know how electricity is made? Use class resources to find out how electricity is made from coal, water, or wind.

- Use the information you gather to draw a series of cartoon panels showing how electricity is made. Label the place that energy is changed from its original form to another form.

- Share your cartoon with your group members who researched a different way that electricity is made. Discuss all the different ways the different forms have in common.

Process Skill: **Sequencing**

Physical Science

28 Magnetic Attraction

- A magnet is a material that attracts objects that contain iron. You have probably used a magnet to attach a piece of paper to your refrigerator door. The refrigerator door contains iron.

- Which objects in your classroom are magnetic? Collect assorted objects from around the classroom. Write the name of each object on a separate piece of paper.

- Use a magnet to find out which objects are magnetic. As a group, sort the pieces of paper into two groups: *Magnetic* and *Not Magnetic*.

- Write about what you can infer about all the objects in the *Magnetic* group.

Process Skill: **Classifying**

Physical Science

25 Using Electricity

- Electricity is electrical energy. It is produced by the movement of charged particles called *electrons*.

- With your group, brainstorm a list of ways that you use electricity every day. Think of appliances or toys that move or make light or heat. Write each idea on a separate piece of paper.

- Does the electricity you use for each task come from a wall outlet or from a battery? As a group, sort the pieces of paper into two piles: *From an Outlet* and *From a Battery*.

- With your group, discuss how your life would be different if your house were not wired for electricity.

Process Skill: **Classifying**

Physical Science

27 Electrical Safety

- We all use electricity in our homes every day. Electricity is very useful. But it can also be very dangerous. An electrical shock can be painful and even deadly.

- Use class resources to find out about electrical safety in the home. List all the dangers. Explain how they can be avoided.

- With your group, create a poster showing what you found out. Use drawings with captions and labels to tell about electrical safety. If you have your teacher's permission, hang the poster in your classroom or in another area of your school.

Process Skill: **Communicating**

Physical Science

Physical Science

Physical Science

Physical Science

Physical Science

30 Sound

- Sound is a form of energy. Sound is produced by vibrating objects. As the objects vibrate, they push on the particles of air that surround them. The air particles move away from the object in waves. When the sound waves reach our ears, we hear a sound.

- With your group, brainstorm a list of familiar sounds. List each sound on a chart. Next to each sound, infer what object was vibrating to make the sound.

32 Light Hitting Objects

- When light rays hit an object, they are absorbed (taken in) by the object, reflected (bounced back) by the object, or transmitted (let pass) through the object. What the light rays do depends on the material of the object they hit.

- Look at a piece of grocery-bag paper, a piece of aluminum foil, and a piece of plastic wrap. As a group, decide which material absorbs the most light, which material reflects the most light, and which material transmits the most light.

- Identify other objects in the classroom and determine whether they absorb, reflect, or transmit light.

29 Magnet Poles

- Every magnet has a north pole and a south pole. The force of magnetism is greatest at a magnet's poles.

- Get two bar magnets with labeled poles. Bring the north pole of one magnet toward the north pole of the other magnet. What happens? Record your observations.

- Now bring the north pole of one magnet toward the south pole of the other magnet. What happens? Record your observations.

- Use your observations to write "The Rules of Magnetic Attraction":

  – "Like poles of magnets _____ each other."

  – "Unlike poles of magnets _____ each other."

31 Light Sources

- Light is a form of energy. It allows us to see all the different things around us. Plants use the energy in sunlight to make food.

- With your group, brainstorm a list of different sources of light. Write each source on a separate piece of paper.

- As a group, sort the pieces of paper into two piles: *Natural Light* and *Artificial Light.*

- Artificial light is made when a different form of energy is changed into light energy. Look at all the pieces of paper in the *Artificial Light* pile. For each, identify the kind of energy that was used to make the light. Write that form of energy on the piece of paper.

Physical Science

Physical Science

Physical Science

Physical Science

Science, Technology, and Society

Materials

Card needing materials other than paper and pencils is:

8—4 kinds of tape (cellophane, masking, cloth, and duct)

Science, Technology, and Society   Card # _____

Science Cooperative Learning CARDS

Your Name: _____

Group Members: _____

Science, Technology, and Society   Card # _____

Science Cooperative Learning CARDS

Your Name: _____

Group Members: _____

- fold -

- fold -

Science, Technology, and Society

1 Technology Everywhere

- Technology is any tool or machine designed to help people in some way. A tool like a shovel may help a person dig a hole. A machine like a computer may help a person process numbers.

- With your group, brainstorm a list of all the different kinds of technology you can think of. Remember that technology includes even the simplest of tools.

- Write the name of each technology on a separate piece of paper. As a group, sort the pieces of paper into different piles according to what features the technologies have in common. The categories you choose are up to you.

Science, Technology, and Society   Process Skill: **Classifying**

2 Technology Help

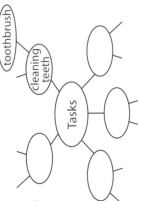

- Technology is any tool or machine designed to help people in some way.

- Think of five tasks you do every day that require the use of technology. Make a concept map on a large piece of paper showing each task and the technologies that you use to complete it.

- Compare your maps with those created by the other members of your group. Do you all use the same technologies to do the same tasks?

Science, Technology, and Society   Process Skill: **Concept Mapping**

3 Scientists and Engineers

- A scientist is someone who studies the natural world. An engineer is someone who designs technology to solve problems. Scientists use technology to help them study science. Engineers use science to help them design technology.

- As a group, make a concept map on a large piece of paper showing the relationship between the following people and things:

  – Scientists
  – Engineers
  – Science
  – Technology

Science, Technology, and Society   Process Skill: **Concept Mapping**

4 Technology Design

- When engineers are developing a new technology, they go through the following steps:
  1) Identify a problem
  2) Think of a solution
  3) Test the solution
  4) Decide if the solution worked
  5) If not, think of a new solution
  6) Share results with others

- As a group, decide on an imaginary problem to solve. Then write about how you might use these steps to solve the problem.

Science, Technology, and Society   Process Skill: **Communicating**

Science, Technology, and Society

Science, Technology, and Society

Science, Technology, and Society

Science, Technology, and Society

5 Scientists Using Technology

- Technology helps scientists in their study of the natural world. It allows them to see objects too small or far away to see with the naked eye. It also allows them to collect samples of materials they couldn't otherwise collect.

- With your group, brainstorm a list of ways that scientists might use technology in their work. Think about the following kinds of scientists: bird biologists, marine biologists, astronomers, geologists, and doctors.

- Make concept maps showing the different technologies used by each kind of scientist, and what those technologies allow the scientist to do.

Science, Technology, and Society   Process Skill: **Generating Ideas**

---

6 Science on the Job

- What do you want to be when you grow up—a chef, a doctor, a gardener, a computer programmer? Scientists aren't the only people who need to understand science in order to do their jobs. Almost every job requires some knowledge of science.

- Write the name of a job you might like to have when you grow up. With your group, brainstorm a list of ways in which that job might require science knowledge. What technologies might you use at this job?

- Continue brainstorming ideas for each member of your group. Did any job not require science or technology?

Science, Technology, and Society   Process Skill: **Generating Ideas**

---

7 Simple or Complicated?

- Some technologies are simple. Others are complicated.

- Consider pumps used to pull water up from a well. The simplest pumps have just a few moving parts and require a person to do the "pumping." More complex pumps have many moving parts. They use fuel to lift the water. Electronic devices control how the pump runs. These pumps require lots of care and can break easily.

- Discuss which pump would be more appropriate for a remote village in Africa where there are no engineers.

- Brainstorm a list of other technologies that work well only in particular situations.

Science, Technology, and Society   Process Skill: **Comparing**

---

8 The Right Technology for the Job

- Collect four different kinds of tape: cellophane (Scotch) tape, masking tape, cloth tape, and duct tape.

- As a group, experiment with each kind of tape. What are the unique qualities of each? Use concept maps to show the different qualities of each kind of tape.

- Review the four concept maps your group created. Use the information in the maps to decide which kind of tape would be the best choice for the following tasks:
  - attaching notes to a refrigerator or wall,
  - wrapping presents with paper,
  - repairing a ripped bike seat, and
  - securing gauze over a cut on your arm.

Science, Technology, and Society Process Skill: **Applying Knowledge**

Science, Technology, and Society

Science, Technology, and Society

Science, Technology, and Society

Science, Technology, and Society

9 Technology in Nature

- When engineers are designing new kinds of technology, they often look to nature for ideas. The sticky feet of a gecko and the waterproof wings of butterflies are just two examples of how nature provides engineers with great ideas for new technologies.

- Imagine that your group is a team of engineers. Use class resources to find pictures of organisms and objects found in nature. Develop an idea for a new technology based on a design in nature.

- As a group, create a poster showing your new technology and the object or idea from nature that inspired it.

Science, Technology, and Society   Process Skill: **Applying Knowledge**

10 Ancient Technology

- Thousands of years ago, people didn't have clocks and watches to tell time. They had to use their observations of things happening around them to keep track of time.

- Imagine that your group is living in Egypt in 1500 B.C. The Pharaoh has asked you to develop a way to track time over the course of a day.

- Brainstorm a list of ideas of ways to tell time. Hint: What changes in nature do you notice from morning to night?

- Write a report or make a poster about your best idea. Include labeled drawings to show how your system works.

Science, Technology, and Society   Process Skill: **Problem Solving**

11 Watering Technology

- Many technologies are designed to do jobs while people are not around.

- Imagine that your class is growing a bean plant. Students water the plant every few days. But a holiday break is coming up and the classroom will be empty for 10 days.

- With your group, come up with an idea for a kind of technology that will water the plant for the class while the students are away. Present the idea in the form of a report or poster. Use labeled drawings to show how the technology would water the plants.

Science, Technology, and Society   Process Skill: **Problem Solving**

12 Feeding Technology

- Many technologies are designed to do jobs while people are not around.

- Imagine that your class has a pet hamster. Students feed the hamster every few days. But a holiday break is coming up and the classroom will be empty for 10 days.

- With your group, come up with an idea for a kind of technology that will feed the hamster for the class while the students are away. Present the idea in the form of a report or poster. Use labeled drawings to show how the technology would feed the hamster.

Science, Technology, and Society   Process Skill: **Problem Solving**

Science, Technology,
and Society

Science, Technology,
and Society

Science, Technology,
and Society

Science, Technology,
and Society

13 Technology Improves Lives

- Technology allows people to live safer, healthier, and more comfortable lives than they did in the past.

- Use class resources to find out how technology has improved life in one of the following areas:
  - Agriculture
  - Health
  - Transportation
  - Sanitation

- As a group, create a poster that shows what your chosen area of life was like a hundred years ago and what it is like today. Use labels to show what role technology has played in the improvement.

Science, Technology, and Society   Process Skill: **Comparing**

14 Telephone Technology

- Technology is always changing. No technology is ever a final solution.

- One good example of how technology changes is the telephone. The telephone is a technology that allows us to talk to people who are some distance away.

- Use class resources to find out the history of telephone technology. What technologies were used to send messages before the telephone? When was the first telephone invented? What changes has it gone through since then?

- As a group, create a series of cartoon panels that show the history of the telephone.

Science, Technology, and Society   Process Skill: **Sequencing**

15 Scientists and Society

- Throughout history, scientists have put forth ideas that were not immediately accepted by members of their societies. Often, the scientists' ideas went against what everyone had always believed to be true. This made it difficult for people to accept the new ideas.

- Use class resources to find out about one of the following scientists:
  - Charles Darwin,
  - Alfred Wegener, or
  - Galileo Galilei.

- As a group, write a report that explains what idea the scientist put forth and why is was rejected at first.

Science, Technology, and Society   Process Skill: **Communicating**

16 World Scientists

- Most of the scientists you read about in school come from Western societies like England, France, or the United States. But people working in other parts of the world have been doing science for thousands of years.

- Use class resources to find out about the history of medicine in one of the following places:
  - China,
  - Africa,
  - India, or
  - South America.

- As a group, write a report of your findings. Use pictures and drawings to illustrate your report.

Science, Technology, and Society   Process Skill: **Communicating**

Science, Technology,
and Society

Science, Technology,
and Society

Science, Technology,
and Society

Science, Technology,
and Society

18 Energy Sources

- Most communities burn fossil fuels, like oil or coal, to make electricity. But fossil fuels are in limited supply, and burning them creates lots of air pollution.

- Imagine that your group has been asked to find out which of the following alternative energy sources might work for your community:
  - Solar energy,
  - Energy from wind, or
  - Energy from water.

- What questions would you need to ask to find out which energy source is best for your community? As a group, write a list of these questions.

Science, Technology, and Society   Process Skill: **Generating Questions**

---

17 Doctor's Promise

- When a person becomes a doctor, he or she is required to take what is called "The Hippocratic Oath." The Hippocratic Oath is a promise that the doctor will never do anything to harm a patient. The oath gets its name from the man who wrote it: Hippocrates, a Greek doctor who lived around 400 B.C. At that time, doctors were forming their own organization with rules.

- Use class resources as needed to learn more about medicine in the time of Hippocrates.

- As a group, discuss the Hippocratic Oath. Why do you suppose it was invented? Why was it important at the time?

Science, Technology, and Society   Process Skill: **Generating Ideas**

20 Water Conservation

- Imagine that your community is facing a water shortage. There is not enough fresh water available to meet the current demands of all the people and businesses in town.

- Use a list of survey questions (see Activity Card 19) to find out how people in your community use water.

- As a group, use the information from the survey to write a list of recommendations for how your community might reduce the amount of water it uses.

- Present your ideas on a poster.

Science, Technology, and Society   Process Skill: **Communicating**

---

19 Water Shortage

- Most of Earth's surface is covered with water. But only a small amount of that is fresh water—water we can use to drink and bathe and water plants.

- Imagine that your community is facing a water shortage. There is not enough fresh water available to meet the current demands of all the people and businesses in town.

- What questions would you need to ask before you could come up with a plan to reduce the amount of water used in your community? As a group, write a list of survey questions for the members of your community.

Science, Technology, and Society   Process Skill: **Generating Questions**

Science, Technology, and Society

Science, Technology, and Society

Science, Technology, and Society

Science, Technology, and Society

21 Energy Shortage

- Most communities burn fossil fuels—like oil or coal—to make electricity. People use electricity to power all kinds of tools and appliances in their homes.
- Imagine that your community is facing an energy shortage. The community cannot produce enough electricity to meet the current demands of all the people and businesses in town.
- What questions would you need to ask before you could come up with a plan to reduce the amount of energy used in your community? As a group, write a list of survey questions for the members of your community.

Science, Technology, and Society   Process Skill: **Generating Questions**

22 Energy Conservation

- Imagine that your community is facing an energy shortage. The community cannot produce enough electricity to meet the current demands of all the people and businesses in town.
- Use a list of survey questions (see Activity Card 21) to find out how people in your community use electricity.
- As a group, use the information from the survey to write a list of recommendations for how your community might reduce the amount of energy it uses.
- Present your ideas in a poster.

Science, Technology, and Society   Process Skill: **Communicating**

23 Air Pollution

- Most communities burn fossil fuels—like oil, coal, and gasoline—to meet their energy needs. But when these fuels are burned, lots of pollutants are released into the air. Other sources of air pollution include wildfires and wood-burning stoves and fireplaces.
- With your group, research what is being done in your community to reduce air pollution. Consider transportation, businesses, and the homes in your community. What else might be done?
- As a group, write a list of recommendations for how your community might further reduce air pollution.
- Present your ideas in a poster.

Science, Technology, and Society   Process Skill: **Generating Ideas**

24 Water Pollution

- Many factories are built next to rivers. The river water is used to cool the factory machines as they work and heat up. The heated water is pumped back out to the river. Unfortunately, plants and animals that live in the river are disturbed by the heated water.
- Imagine that a company wants to build a factory on a river that runs through your community. Some people say it will help the town by creating lots of jobs. Others argue that the wildlife in the river will be harmed.
- Use class resources to find out more. Then hold a debate within your group. Two people should argue for the factory, and two should argue against it.

Science, Technology, and Society   Process Skill: **Communicating**

Science, Technology, and Society

Science, Technology, and Society

Science, Technology, and Society

Science, Technology, and Society

25 Building a Dam

- Imagine that a group of people want to build a dam across a river in your community. The dam will allow the people to control the flow of water down the river. It will also generate electricity for the town.

- When a dam is built across a river, water backs up behind the dam and forms a lake. This change affects all the plants and animals that live in or near the river.

- With your group, make a concept map on a large piece of paper showing what physical changes might result from the building of a dam. Then extend the map to show what organisms might be affected and how.

Science, Technology, and Society   Process Skill: **Concept Mapping**

26 Managing a Forest

- The job of forest scientists is to keep the forests healthy. But not all forest scientists agree on the best way to do this.

- Some forest scientists think that forests should be left alone. No trees should be removed, and wildfires should be left to burn. Other scientists think that some trees should be cleared out of forests to prevent strong fires from burning all the trees.

- Use class resources to find out more. Then hold a debate within your group. Two people should argue for leaving the forests alone, and two should argue for some clearing.

Science, Technology, and Society   Process Skill: **Communicating**

27 Drilling for Oil

- People in the United States use a lot of oil. We use it to heat our homes, run our cars, power our appliances, run our factories, and so on. Unfortunately, we are using more oil than we have. As a result, we have to buy it from other countries.

- Scientists know that there is oil under the ground in Alaska. Many people think that we should drill in Alaska for more oil. Others think that we should not because Alaska is home to lots of wild animals.

- Use class resources to find out more. Then hold a debate within your group. Two people should argue for drilling, and two should argue against it.

Science, Technology, and Society   Process Skill: **Communicating**

28 Building an Airport

- People count on airplanes to take them places they want to go. But airplanes make a lot of noise, and runways take up a lot of space. No one wants to live next to an airport.

- Imagine that a committee of people want to build an airport in your state. They are looking around for the best place to put the airport.

- With your group, write a list of questions the committee should consider before choosing a site for the new airport.

Science, Technology, and Society Process Skill: **Generating Questions**

Science, Technology, and Society

Science, Technology, and Society

Science, Technology, and Society

Science, Technology, and Society

29 Using Pesticides

- Pesticides are poisonous chemicals used to kill insects that eat valuable trees or plants. These chemicals kill unwanted insects, but they can also harm other living things. The chemicals can even get into the water supply and end up in our drinking water.

- Imagine that a committee of people in your community wants to spray your local park with pesticides to get rid of a kind of caterpillar that is eating all the tree leaves.

- With your group, write a list of questions that the committee should consider before spraying the park.

Science, Technology, and Society Process Skill: **Generating Questions**

---

30 Antibacterial Soap

- Antibacterial soap is soap that contains a chemical that kills bacteria. Antibacterial soap was designed to kill bacteria that might be on our hands. Since bacteria can make us sick, antibacterial soap seemed like a good idea.

- Unfortunately, some bacteria are not killed by the soap. These bacteria live and reproduce. Soon, bacteria that can't be killed by the chemicals in antibacterial soap begin to take over.

- Hold a debate with your group. Two people should argue for using antibacterial soap, and two should argue against using it.

Science, Technology, and Society Process Skill: **Communicating**

---

31 Engineering Food

- Every year, much of the food grown around the world is eaten by pests. In order to reduce the amount of food lost to pests, scientists have engineered certain fruits and vegetables in the laboratory to be resistant to pests.

- Many people think that engineered foods are not natural and are not a good idea. They are afraid of the risks involved with growing engineered plants.

- Use class resources to learn more about the benefits and risks of engineered foods (often called "genetically modified foods"). Then hold a debate within your group. Two people should argue for engineered plants, and two should argue against it.

Science, Technology, and Society Process Skill: **Communicating**

---

32 Cloning

- Ethics is the study of values—what is good and what is bad. Many questions about science and technology involve ethics. Cloning is a good example.

- Cloning is the creation of an exact copy of a living thing. Scientists use the genes found in the cells of one animal to create an exact copy of the animal. Many people feel that cloning is not ethical. Others think the benefits of cloning outweigh the ethical questions.

- Use class resources to learn more about the arguments surrounding cloning. Then hold a debate within your group. Two people should argue for cloning, and two should argue against it.

Science, Technology, and Society Process Skill: **Communicating**

Science, Technology, and Society

Science, Technology, and Society

Science, Technology, and Society

Science, Technology, and Society